THE BABY-SITTERS CLUB®

DAWN AND THE IMPOSSIBLE THREE

**DON'T MISS THE OTHER
BABY-SITTERS CLUB GRAPHIC NOVELS!**

ANN M. MARTIN

THE BABY-SITTERS CLUB

DAWN AND THE IMPOSSIBLE THREE

A GRAPHIC NOVEL BY

GALE GALLIGAN

WITH COLOR BY BRADEN LAMB

An Imprint of

SCHOLASTIC

Text copyright © 2017, by Ann M. Martin
Art copyright © 2017 by Gale Galligan

Library of Congress Control Number: 2016960080

ISBN 978-1-338-06730-9 (hardcover)
ISBN 978-1-338-06711-8 (paperback)

20 19 18 17 16 15 14 13   21

Printed in China   95
First edition, Octorber 2017

Edited by Cassandra Pelham and David Levithan
Book design by Phil Falco
Creative Director: David Saylor

For Aunt Dot
A. M.M.

Eternal thanks to Mon, Dad, Lori, A. M. M.,
Raina Telgemeier, Cassandra Pelham, David Saylor,
David Levithan, Phil Falco, Sheila Marie Everett , Braden Lamb,
John Green, Dave Roman, Rachel Young, Ngozi Ukazu,
Dave Valeza, and all my beloved friends,
family, and grads.

And to Patrick, who gets his very own line
because he is my favorite boy.
G. G.

KRISTY THOMAS
PRESIDENT

CLAUDIA KISHI
VICE PRESIDENT

DAWN SCHAFER
ALTERNATE OFFICER

MARY ANNE SPIER
SECRETARY

STACEY MCGILL
TREASURER

1

3

WHAT'S EIGHT TIMES SEVEN?

HI, MAL. YOU KNOW THAT ONE.

THIS IS MALLORY.

...

FIFTY-SIX?

SHE'S HELPED US BABY-SIT BEFORE.

RIGHT!

THANKS! THAT'S ALL I HAD LEFT.

SNACK TIME??

SURE.

whoosh

IN FACT, TODAY WILL BE HER FIRST DAY AS AN OFFICIAL JUNIOR MEMBER OF THE BSC.

AT LEAST IT'S NOT AS BAD AS NICKY'S FINGER.

glug

WHAT'S THAT?

A FEW MONTHS AGO, I WAS BABY-SITTING THE BOYS AND THEY WERE PLAYING VOLLEYBALL.

NICKY LOOKED AWAY FOR A MOMENT AND...

BAM! THE BALL SLAMMED INTO HIS FINGER.

IT WAS IN A CAST FOR MONTHS.

I TOOK CARE OF ALL THE KIDS WHILE MOM AND DAD DROVE NICKY TO THE EMERGENCY ROOM.

THIS HAPPENED WHEN YOU WERE IN CHARGE OF HIM?

I MEAN, IT WAS AN ACCIDENT.

WHAT? WHAT IS IT?

DAD JUST CALLED.

HE SAID NOT TO EXPECT HIM FOR DINNER TONIGHT.

SO?

HE SAID NOT TO EXPECT HIM... BECAUSE HE'S TAKING YOUR MOM OUT!

twirl

OH! ANOTHER DATE!!

DAD **NEVER** USED TO DO SPUR-OF-THE-MOMENT THINGS.

BUT HE SAID HE GOT THE IDEA ABOUT FIVE MINUTES AGO!

I CAN'T BELIEVE IT.

I KNOW...
I LEFT SOME...

RIGHT AROUND HERE...

THIS IS CLAUDIA, OUR VICE PRESIDENT.

YES!

yummi

STACEY'S OUR TREASURER. SHE MOVED HERE FROM NEW YORK CITY A LITTLE WHILE BEFORE I CAME.

WE'RE UP TO FOURTEEN DOLLARS.

NOT BAD.

MAYBE WE SHOULD GET MORE STUFF FOR THE KID-KITS?

KRISTY IS THE CLUB'S FOUNDER AND PRESIDENT.

SHE DIDN'T LIKE ME MUCH AT FIRST, BUT I THINK WE'RE ALL RIGHT NOW.

AM I LATE?

15

ONLY ONE
EARRING

RUBBER
BAND

PRICE
TAG

MOM, FOR
HEAVEN'S SAKE.

WHAT WOULD
I DO WITHOUT
YOU, DAWN?

snap

MUCH BETTER.
AND I'M OFF!

ALL RIGHT,
SAY HI TO
MR. SPIER
FOR --

. . .

EARRING!

UUUUGH.

LEFTOVER STEW.

C'MON, C'MON.

HEY, JEFF!

ORGANIC FROZEN PIZZA?

YES, PLEASE.

ding!

ring
rin

ring ring

BOOOOO.

HI. WHAT'S ALL THIS STUFF?

DAWN BROUGHT IT OVER.

DAD'S LETTING ME TAKE THE OLD STUFF OFF MY WALLS AND PUT UP WHATEVER I WANT!

HE'S LETTING YOU PUT **THUMBTACKS** IN THE **WALLS?**

I GUESS SO.

HOW COME YOU DIDN'T TELL **ME** YOU WERE GOING TO START REDECORATING?

I DON'T KNOW...

HEY, DID I TELL YOU? OUR PARENTS WENT ON ANOTHER DATE LAST NIGHT...

A **SPONTANEOUS** ONE.

OH...THAT'S COOL, I GUESS.

YOU KNOW...

29

I MIGHT HAVE SOME THINGS YOU COULD USE, TOO.

REMEMBER WHEN WE MADE THAT POSTER FOR ART CLASS AND IT WON THE PRIZE?

YOU STILL *HAVE THAT?*

AND I BET WE COULD USE WATSON'S STENCIL KIT TO FIX UP YOUR OLD PINK PHOTO FRAMES!

OH, WHAT A *WONDERFUL* IDEA!

AND WITH ALL OF THESE FREE DECORATIONS, GOSH!

MAYBE I *CAN* CONVINCE DAD TO REPLACE THE BEDSPREAD.

HEY, KRISTY, DO YOU REMEMBER THE TIME...

AFTER THAT, THE THREE OF US WORKED ON MARY ANNE'S ROOM FOR HOURS. WE TALKED AND PLANNED AND LAUGHED.

BUT I NOTICED TWO THINGS:

KRISTY ONLY SPOKE DIRECTLY TO MARY ANNE...

AND KRISTY NEVER LAUGHED AT MY JOKES. (EVEN THOUGH MARY ANNE DID.)

BEFORE I KNEW IT, THE TIME HAD COME FOR MY FIRST OFFICIAL BABY-SITTING JOB WITH THE BARRETTS.

CHAPTER 4

ding dong

creeeeak

HI, SUZI. I'M DAWN. I FIXED YOUR KNEE, REMEMBER?

nod

WELL, I'M GOING TO BABY-SIT FOR YOU TODAY.

IS YOUR MOM HOME?

nod

AND SO, I DEFEATED ANOTHER STUDENT...

MAY I COME IN?

nod

OF THE NOTORIOUS **SCHOOL OF NODS.**

OH, IS THIS MARNIE?

YEAH.

HI, MARNIE. YOU SURE ARE CU--

WHOOF.

DO YOU KNOW WHERE YOUR MOM KEEPS THE DIAPERS?

shrug

IT WAS ABOUT THEN THAT I NOTICED...

34

THIS PLACE WAS A MESS!!

tmp tmp tmp

DAWN? DAWN, IS THAT YOU?

HI, MRS. BARRETT.

WHERE DO YOU KEEP YOUR—

SO LONG, DARLINGS. BE GOOD FOR DAWN.

WAIT! WHERE ARE YOU GOING TO BE?

AT A JOB INTERVIEW. AND I'M LATE.

WHAT IF THERE'S AN EMERGENCY? HOW DO I REACH YOU?

CALL THE PIKES, OKAY?

WELL...

ALL RIGHT.

SCREEEEEEE

USUALLY, I GET SOME KIND OF SPECIAL INSTRUCTION.

SNACK TIME AT 4, NO TV BEFORE HOMEWORK...

UH...

SOMETHING.

YOU GUYS EVER SEE *MARY POPPINS*?

NOPE.

WELL...HOW WOULD YOU LIKE TO PLAY A GAME?

YEAH!!

THIS SURE IS NICER, ISN'T IT?

YEAH!

EVEN THOUGH WE DIDN'T BEAT THE RECORD THIS TIME.

HEY, DAWN?

YEAH?

DO YOU HAVE A DADDY?

WELL...YES. BUT NOT HERE. HE DOESN'T LIVE WITH US.

YEAH. HE'S IN CALIFORNIA. THREE THOUSAND MILES AWAY.

REALLY?

MY MOM AND DAD ARE DIVORCED.

SO ARE OURS.

43

BY THE TIME MRS. BARRETT CAME BACK...

SUZI HAD COOLED OFF.

AND WE WERE ALL EXCITED TO SHOW OFF OUR HANDIWORK.

YOU'RE A **WONDER,** DAWN!

I HOPE YOU'LL COME BACK.

ANY TIME.

IF I HAD ONLY KNOWN HOW OFTEN "ANY TIME" WAS GOING TO BE, I MIGHT NOT HAVE SPOKEN SO QUICKLY.

44

THE FIRST TIME I MET MARY ANNE, SHE WAS SITTING AT A CAFETERIA TABLE ALL BY HERSELF. THE BABY-SITTERS CLUB HAD JUST HAD A HUGE FIGHT.

THEY WERE ALL SITTING WITH OTHER FRIENDS -- EXCEPT FOR MARY ANNE.

THAT'S WHERE I CAME IN.

NOW THAT SHE AND KRISTY ARE FRIENDS AGAIN...

THEY'VE GONE BACK TO SITTING AT THEIR USUAL TABLE WITH THE SHILLABER TWINS.

I NEVER THOUGHT OF THAT.

ME NEITHER.

I DID.

I'D HAVE A BROTHER **AND** A SISTER!

I'VE ALWAYS WANTED A SISTER.

I THOUGHT I WAS LIKE YOUR SISTER.

SUDDENLY, I KNEW.

KRISTY DIDN'T DISLIKE ME.

...AND THEY'LL GET MARRIED AND HAVE A BIG, BEAUTIFUL WEDDING, WITH TONS OF FLOWERS...

AND A **HUUUGE** CAKE!

SHE WAS JUST AFRAID OF BEING LEFT OUT.

HEY, um, KRISTY.

AREN'T YOUR MOM AND WATSON PLANNING TO GET MARRIED SOON?

UM...YEAH. IN THE FALL, PROBABLY.

AND THEN YOU'LL HAVE A LITTLE STEPSISTER AND STEPBROTHER, RIGHT?

RIGHT. PLUS MY THREE BROTHERS.

GOSH, YOU'RE GOING TO BE A BIG FAMILY.

YEAH! FOUR BROTHERS AND YOUR FIRST SISTER.

HOW'S EVERYBODY GOING TO FIT IN YOUR HOUSE?

OH, WELL...

WE'RE... SORT OF MOVING.

TO WATSON'S MANSION.

OOOOH, A REAL **MANSION?**

A REAL MANSION.

IT'S **HUGE.**

DO YOU GET TO REDECORATE YOUR ROOM? LIKE, HOWEVER YOU WANT?

I GUESS. BUT WHAT I REALLY WANT IS EXACTLY WHAT'S IN MY ROOM RIGHT NOW.

WHAAAAT? YOU'VE HAD THAT FOR **YEARS.**

JUST THINK! YOU COULD PROBABLY DO ANYTHING YOU WANTED TO YOUR NEW ROOM.

SPORTS THEMED...

YOUR FAVORITE COLORS...

OR EVEN SOMETHING HIGH TECH --

WHAT I **WANT** IS WHAT I'VE GOT.

SO LAY OFF, OKAY?

OKAY!

SEE YOU GUYS LATER.

LATER.

DAWN! GOOD MORNING! EMERGENCY NUMBER ON THE FRIDGE --

GOT TO RUN --

I'LL SEE YOU TONIGHT!!

whoosh

HOW LONG ARE YOU STAYING?

WHAT'S FOR BREAKFAST?

MOH?

UH --

ring ring

HOLD THOSE THOUGHTS.

HELLO, BARRETT RESIDENCE.

DAAAAWN!

CLAUDIA? IS THAT YOU?

YEAH!

STACEY, MALLORY, AND I ARE SITTING FOR THE PIKES -- ALL OF THEM -- AND WE'RE THINKING ABOUT HAVING A PICNIC.

WHAT TIME?

LET'S SAY... 1:00?

WE'LL DO LUNCH, YOU BRING SNACKS?

YEAH! PERFECT.

BUT WE'D NEED TO HUSTLE!

9:00 – Breakfast.

9:30 – Clean table.

10:00 – Kids get dressed.

10:30 – Straighten bedrooms.

11:00 – Still straightening rooms.

11:30 – Snacks for picnic??

AHA!

Brownie Mix
Just Like M

12:00 – ~~Playtime~~ Clean kitchen.

POMF

Flour

12:30 – Brownies!

12:50 – Head over to picnic!

STACEY.

PSSSST.
STACEY.

DAWN! YOU MADE IT!

UH...ARE YOU OKAY?

HOW MANY PIKE KIDS ARE THERE?

EIGHT. YOU KNOW THAT.

RIGHT, AND THERE ARE THREE BARRETT KIDS.

AND YOU AND ME AND CLAUDIA.

SO... FOURTEEN.

NOW COUNT THE PEOPLE IN THE BACKYARD.

BZZZZZZ.

HEY!

CLAUDIA! JORDAN GAVE ME THE BIZZER SIGN!

OH NO.

WHAT?

THE PIKE KIDS MADE IT UP. IT'S LIKE... AN INSULT OR SOMETHING?

JUST IGNORE HIM.

BUT HE GAVE ME THE **BIZZER** SIGN!

BZZZZZZZZZZZ.

BIZZERS DON'T GET BROWNIES!!

THAT WAS A CLOSE ONE.

HEY, MARNIE. YOU WANT A BROWNIE?

STOP!!

WHAT ARE YOU DOING?!

WHAT ARE YOU DOING?!

MARNIE'S ALLERGIC.

SHE CAN'T EAT CHOCOLATE. IT MAKES HER REALLY SICK.

WHAT...? BUT...

MRS. BARRETT NEVER TOLD ME THAT.

63

Wednesday, May 27th

This evning I babysat for Dawn Shafers brother Jeff. I could tell he thoght he was to old for a baby-sitter but Dawn was sitting at the Barretts and her mom had suddenly gotten tickits to a concert and Mrs. Shaffer didnt want to leave Jeff alone at night. She called me at the last minute and luckly I was free. Sitting for Jeff was an easy job.

But! Dawn I noticed this is the second night in a row you've sat at the Baretts. And I looked in our apontment book and you were their four times last week. Maybe you are over doing it?

I am telling you this as a freind.

* Claudia *

SORRY! GOTTA GO! BARRETTS!

CLAUDIA WAS RIGHT.

WITH MRS. BARRETT'S DIVORCE AND JOB HUNT, IT SEEMED LIKE SHE ALWAYS NEEDED SOMEONE TO LOOK AFTER THE KIDS...

AND THEY LIKED ME BEST.

ONE TIME, I EVEN MISSED A MEETING OF THE BABY-SITTERS CLUB.

MRS. BARRETT HAD PROMISED SHE'D BE BACK BY 5:30, BUT ENDED UP STAYING OUT UNTIL 6 WITHOUT SO MUCH AS A CALL!

BUT I DID FINALLY GET UP THE NERVE TO TALK TO HER.

THANK YOU, DAWN. I DON'T KNOW WHAT I'D DO --

MRS. BARRETT?

HOW COME YOU DIDN'T TELL ME MARNIE'S ALLERGIC TO CHOCOLATE?

I...DIDN'T TELL YOU?

NO.

I ALMOST GAVE HER A PIECE OF BROWNIE THE OTHER DAY. MALLORY STOPPED ME JUST IN TIME.

MY GOODNESS!

DO THE KIDS HAVE ANY OTHER ALLERGIES?

NONE THAT WE'RE AWARE OF.

IS THERE ANYTHING ELSE I SHOULD KNOW?

JUST ONE THING. IF MY EX-HUSBAND EVER CALLS...

DON'T LET HIM **TALK** TO THE CHILDREN.

DON'T TELL HIM HE CAN **SEE** THE CHILDREN.

AND **DON'T** TELL HIM I'M OUT.

JUST SAY YOU'RE HELPING ME AND I'M BUSY. HE --

crash thnk

EEEEK!

SUZI!

KIDS...

I'LL TAKE CARE OF IT. WHY DON'T YOU DRY SUZI OFF?

BUDDY, GO GET THE PAPER TOWELS. WE'LL CLEAN UP.

AWWW.

THANK YOU AGAIN, DAWN. I HOPE YOU KNOW HOW MUCH WE APPRECIATE YOU.

WITH EVERYTHING THAT'S BEEN GOING ON, WELL, I JUST --

hug

ring

I'LL GET IT!

BUDDY! I TOLD YOU, YOU ARE NOT TO ANSWER THE -- !

DAD SAYS WHERE ARE WE?

YOU WERE S'POSED TO DROP OFF ME AND SUZI HALF AN HOUR AGO.

OH GRACIOUS, I COMPLETELY FORGOT!!

DAWN, I'LL SEE YOU WEDNESDAY!

SO THAT DIDN'T REALLY GO AS PLANNED.

IT'S BEEN A FEW WEEKS NOW, AND LIKE CLAUDIA SAID, I'VE BEEN SITTING FOR THE BARRETTS A **LOT.**

IT'S STARTING TO FEEL LIKE I'M, I DON'T KNOW, A STAND-IN MOM.

BUDDY? WHAT'S THE MATTER?

sniffle

m-MY HOMEWORK.

WELL, CAN I HELP? I'M PRETTY SMART.

I NEED **MOM'S** HELP.

THAT WASN'T THE WORST I HAD TO DEAL WITH, THOUGH.

URGHHHHHHH.

HWORKKK

AH!

WHERE IS IT, WHERE IS IT...

milk

~~butter~~

appt. 307

Emergency-cell #
~~362.3015~~

5:30
up kids

ring
ring

HI! I'M AWAY FROM MY PHONE RIGHT NOW, BUT LEAVE YOUR NAME AND NUMBER...

HER PHONE WAS OFF.

SHE ALWAYS FORGETS TO TURN IT ON.

hrrrr
rrrkk

wahhhhh

hwork!

wahhhhhh
hworkkkk
ah   hhl
k9gu
1k99

HELLO?

MALLORY! THANK YOU SO MUCH FOR COMING.

SUZI'S BEEN THROWING UP AND I CAN'T GET AHOLD OF MRS. BARRETT. COULD YOU...?

I'M ON IT.

I SPENT THE REST OF THE DAY READING TO SUZI IN THE BATHROOM...

WHILE MALLORY TOOK CARE OF MARNIE AND BUDDY.

beep
toktoktok

WHAT'S GOTTEN INTO YOU?

I WAS GLAD I COULD HELP, BUT BUDDY'S MOM SHOULD HAVE BEEN THE ONE HELPING HIM WITH HIS FAMILY TREE...

ding dong

sigh

BEING PROUD OF THE GOLD STAR...

HELLO, DAWN.

COME ON UPSTAIRS.

AND GETTING THE HUG.

THANKS, JANINE.

THE REST OF THE MEETING WAS PRETTY NORMAL, UNTIL...

OH, BEFORE I FORGET...

KRISTY, I WANTED TO ASK YOU ABOUT SOMETHING.

WHAT?

I WAS BABY-SITTING FOR DAVID MICHAEL THE OTHER DAY...

YEAH, I REMEMBER.

UM... STACEY?

Pant Pant

WHEN YOU MOVED, DID THEY PACK UP **EVERYTHING** IN THE VAN?

OH, OF COURSE. EVERY LAST THING.

THEY DIDN'T LEAVE **ANYTHING** BEHIND.

E-EVEN YOUR PETS??

???

Snuffle

OH, DAVID MICHAEL!

THEY WON'T PUT **LOUIE** IN THE VAN.

hahahaha

DAVID MICHAEL!

BUT TALKING TO HIM GOT ME THINKING.

WHAT ARE WE GOING TO DO ABOUT THE CLUB WHEN YOU MOVE?

IT'S ONLY A FEW MILES AWAY --

MOM WON'T LET ME BIKE HERE FROM WATSON'S.

COULD WE MEET SOMEWHERE ELSE?

BUT WE'D NEED A PHONE.

OUR CLIENTS HAVE TO KNOW WHERE TO REACH US.

STUPID, STUPID WATSON.

HEY, DON'T GET DOWN ON WATSON. IT'S NOT HIS FAULT.

IT'S NOT ANYBODY'S FAULT.

A LOT **YOU** KNOW.

I MAY KNOW MORE THAN YOU THINK.

YOU'RE NOT THE ONLY ONE WHOSE PARENTS GOT DIVORCED.

NO, BUT I'M THE ONLY ONE WHOSE MOM CHOSE TO GET MARRIED TO A GUY WHO'S SO RICH HE LIVES OVER ON **MILLIONAIRE'S LANE.**

AND **I'M** THE ONLY ONE WHO MAY HAVE TO DROP OUT OF THE CLUB. THE CLUB **I** STARTED.

KRISTY!

WE COULDN'T RUN THE CLUB WITHOUT YOU. IT WOULDN'T BE RIGHT.

CHAPTER 9

THE FATE OF THE CLUB WAS HANGING IN THE AIR -- MUCH LIKE THE WINTER CHILL THAT JUST WOULDN'T GO AWAY.

BUT IT WAS MEMORIAL DAY WEEKEND, AND MOM WAS DETERMINED TO HOST A PICNIC.

MOM, THIS MIGHT BE THE FIRST PICNIC EVER ATTENDED BY PEOPLE IN DOWN JACKETS.

FOR PITY'S SAKE, DAWN. IT'S LOVELY OUT.

INCOMING!

ACK!

SPlsh.

OF COURSE, MOST PEOPLE ALREADY HAD PLANS. IN THE END, THE ONLY ONES WHO COULD MAKE IT WERE MY GRANDPARENTS, THE SPIERS, THE BARRETTS...

DO YOU THINK I COULD SUBSTITUTE RAW HONEY FOR SUGAR?

UM...

AND KRISTY AND DAVID MICHAEL.

WHAT IF, INSTEAD OF TRYING TO MAKE ALL THIS FANCY STUFF, WE JUST DO HAMBURGERS, HOT DOGS, AND POTATO SALAD?

HOT DOGS! DO YOU EVEN KNOW WHAT'S IN A --

WE'RE IN CONNECTICUT NOW, MOM.

PEOPLE **BARBECUE** THINGS HERE. WE SHOULD TRY TO SERVE FOOD THEY'LL EAT.

SOON...

KEEP AN EYE ON THEM. THIS IS A GOOD CHANCE TO SEE HOW THEY'RE DOING.

AND WHETHER OR NOT YOUR GRANDPARENTS STILL DISAPPROVE OF MY DAD.

WE MIGHT HAVE TO AVERT A **CRISIS**.

HEY...

I'M GLAD EVERYTHING TURNED OUT OKAY.

YEAH.

YOUR PARENTS REALLY LIKE EACH OTHER.

YOU MIGHT ACTUALLY END UP BEING SISTERS.

KRISTY...

ARE YOU ALL RIGHT?

I...

WELL, YOU KNOW.

MY MOM GETTING MARRIED, AND THE MOVE AND ALL. IT'S A LOT.

I'M GOING TO BE SO FAR AWAY FROM YOU GUYS, AND I DON'T KNOW WHAT'S HAPPENING WITH THE CLUB...

sniffle

YOU DON'T WANT TO BE LEFT BEHIND.

WHEN WE MOVED HERE, WE HAD TO LEAVE A LOT BEHIND.

OUR HOUSE, OUR COUSINS AND BEST FRIENDS, DAD...

THEY'RE ALL THOUSANDS OF MILES AWAY NOW.

BUT WE STILL TALK ALL THE TIME.

YOU'RE ONLY MOVING ACROSS TOWN. DO YOU REALLY THINK WE'RE GOING TO LET OUR FRIENDSHIP CHANGE OVER A FEW MILES?

Tuesday, June 2

This afternoon I baby-sat for Buddy, Suzi, and Marnie Barrett. What a time I had! I don't know if it's the weather or problems with the divorce or what, but the kids were wild. Wild and cranky. I'm sure the sitter they really wanted was Dawn. I don't know how you handle them, Dawn. I hope they behave better for you than they do for me.

By the way, there was a really strange phone call from Mr. Barrett today, wanting to know where Buddy was. I wouldn't give him any information. When I told Mrs. Barrett about the call, she turned purple (not really) and said he shouldn't have called when he knew darn well she'd be out. What's going on?

I think we should all be careful of calls from Mr. Barrett.

Mary Anne

CHAPTER 10

TODAY, FOR THE FIRST TIME IN AGES, I WASN'T THE ONE BABY-SITTING FOR THE BARRETTS.

I DIDN'T ENVY MARY ANNE -- IT HAD BEEN RAINING FOR THREE DAYS STRAIGHT.

PEW!

PEW!

I GOT YOU! YOU'RE DEAD!

WELL, I'M NOT DEAD FOR LONG, BECAUSE I'M COMING INTO YOUR HOUSE.

STAND ASIDE, MARTIAN MAN.

MARTIAN?! I'M A COWBOY! FROM VENUS!

THIS IS OBVIOUSLY A VENUS WEAPON!

DAWN?

ALL RIGHT, WHO WANTS TO --

BIZZ

BUDDY, YOU GIVE ONE MORE BIZZER SIGN TO ANYONE TODAY -- **ANYONE** -- AND YOU'LL HAVE TO STAY IN YOUR ROOM UNTIL YOUR MOTHER COMES HOME.

WILL **NOT.**

YES, YOU WILL. I'M IN CHARGE HERE, AND WHAT I SAY GOES.

WILL YOU TELL MOM IF I'M BAD?

I MIGHT.

TATTLETALE!

THAT'S THE WAY IT IS.

NOW, YOU KNOW WHAT WE'RE GOING TO DO TODAY?

NOT READ.

NOT COLOR.

NOT WATCH TV.

NOT PLAY CANDY LAND.

NOPE. I CAN TELL YOU'RE TIRED OF THE SAME OLD RAINY-DAY STUFF.

SO TODAY WE'RE GOING TO GO OUTSIDE FOR A **PUDDLE WALK.**

JUMP IN AS MANY PUDDLES AS YOU CAN.

TRY TO MAKE BIG SPLASHES!

aaaaAAA

AAAACK!

SPLOOSH

HE **SPLASHED** ME!

GOOD!

YOU'RE WEARING YOUR SWIMSUIT AND RAINCOAT.

THESE CLOTHES ARE **SUPPOSED** TO GET WET.

OHHHHHHHH.

tmp
tmp

giggle

OKAY, LET'S JUST LEAVE OUR FLIP-FLOPS BY THE --

ring ring ri

SPACE PHONE!

HOLD ON!

NOOOOO! VENUS **NEEDS** ME!

HELLO, BARRETT RESIDENCE.

BZZZZZZ

BUDDY! I TOLD YOU WHAT WOULD HAPPEN IF YOU DID THAT AGAIN.

GO TO YOUR ROOM.

SORRY ABOUT THAT. HELLO?

HELLO? WHO'S THIS?

stomp

Stomp

THIS IS MARY ANNE SPIER, THE SITTER. WHO'S THIS?

THIS IS MR. BARRETT.

WOULD YOU MIND PUTTING BUDDY ON?

OR SUZI?

I'M SORRY, THEY'RE...AT A FRIEND'S HOUSE.

OH, **FINE.**

Slam

beep beep beep

WHEN MRS. BARRETT GOT HOME, THERE WAS QUITE THE SCENE.

BUDDY WAS MAD BECAUSE HE'D BEEN PUNISHED...

MRS. BARRETT WAS MAD BECAUSE BUDDY HAD MISBEHAVED...

AND SHE WAS **VERY** UPSET THAT MR. BARRETT HAD CALLED.

HE'S ONLY SUPPOSED TO SPEAK TO THE KIDS ON ALTERNATING TUESDAYS, AND THIS IS THE WRONG DAY.

IT'S PART OF THE CUSTODY ARRANGEMENT, AND HE CAN'T KEEP HIS OWN **SCHEDULE** STRAIGHT!

AND BUDDY, WHAT IS THE **MATTER** WITH YOU?

I GET NOTES FROM YOUR TEACHER, YOU GIVE MARY ANNE TROUBLE...

I DON'T HAVE **TIME** FOR THIS, YOUNG MAN.

I CANNOT BE YOUR MOTHER AND FATHER, RUN THIS HOUSEHOLD, LOOK FOR A JOB...

AND STRAIGHTEN OUT THE MESSES YOU GET YOURSELF INTO.

IT'S TOO MUCH TO ASK OF ANYBODY.

THE RAIN DIDN'T LET UP AFTER THAT.

I DIDN'T REALLY MIND. IT MADE ME THINK OF THE RAINY SEASON IN CALIFORNIA.

PLUS, MY MOM WAS IN A GREAT MOOD.

SHE AND MR. SPIER WERE TALKING ON THE PHONE ALMOST EVERY NIGHT.

AND I HADN'T HAD TO TELL HER TO FIX HER EARRINGS IN **THREE DAYS STRAIGHT** -- A NEW RECORD.

TOO BAD THE BARRETT KIDS WEREN'T NEARLY AS HIGH-SPIRITED.

WAIT!

HOLD ON A SEC. WE'VE GOTTA BE SMART.

BUDDY, YOU'RE READY AS SOON AS YOU PUT ON YOUR BOOTS.

SO YOU CAN GO AHEAD.

BUT, SUZI AND MARNIE, IT'S CHILLY OUT TODAY. WE HAVE TO GET YOU BUNDLED UP FIRST.

NO FAIR!!

IT'LL ONLY BE A MINUTE. BUDDY, BOOTS AND JACKET.

OKAYYYY!

grumble

114

BUDDY?

BUDDY?

BUDDY?

BUDDYYYY!

BUDDY? NO, HE HASN'T BEEN BY.

I WAS HOPING HE'D COME SEE MY NEW WALKIE-TALKIES, THOUGH.

TRY CALLING THE MURPHYS. AND THE SPENCERS.

AND LET ME KNOW IF YOU DON'T FIND HIM IN ABOUT HALF AN HOUR.

WHERE ON EARTH COULD BUDDY HAVE GONE?

WHEN WE GOT BACK, WE CHECKED THE YARD AND HOUSE ONE MORE TIME, AND THEN I STARTED MAKING CALLS.

I CALLED THE MURPHYS AND THE SPENCERS, LIKE MRS. PIKE SUGGESTED, AND THEN FOUR MORE NEIGHBORS WHOSE NUMBERS MR. MURPHY GAVE ME.

IF YOU SEE HIM, COULD YOU LET ME KNOW?

UH-HUH.

THANK YOU.

TO MAKE MATTERS WORSE, I COULDN'T GET AHOLD OF MRS. BARRETT.

HI! I CAN'T COME TO THE PHONE RIGHT NOW, BUT --

click

BUDDY WAS MY RESPONSIBILITY, AND I'D LET HIM DOWN.

WHAT? WHERE IS HE??

HE'S AT HIS LESSON.

HUH?

SUZI, DOES BUDDY TAKE ANY KIND OF LESSONS? LIKE PIANO OR ART?

UH...

NO...?

HONEY, WHAT MAKES YOU THINK BUDDY IS AT A LESSON?

WELL...

AT THE SAME TIME MRS. KATZ AND SANDY PICKED ME UP FOR MY PIANO LESSON...

I SAW SOMEONE PICK BUDDY UP.

SO I THOUGHT...

YOU SAW BUDDY GET INTO A CAR WITH SOMEONE THIS MORNING?

nod

I'M GOING TO CALL THE POLICE.

BUDDY!

BUDDYYYYYY...!!

DO YOU REMEMBER ANYTHING ELSE ABOUT THE CAR?

UM...

DID YOU SEE THE LICENSE PLATE? THE DRIVER?

I DON'T...

WAS IT A MAN OR A WOMAN?

I DON'T **KNOW**, OKAY?

WE LIVE THREE HOUSES AWAY, AND BESIDES, I WASN'T PAYING ATTENTION.

I DIDN'T THINK THERE WAS ANY **REASON** TO.

MRS. KATZ PICKED ME UP, AND I SAW BUDDY GET INTO A CAR IN HIS DRIVEWAY. THAT'S **ALL.**

BUT YOU'RE SURE IT WAS A BLUE CAR.

YEAH.

A BLUE CAR.

AND YOU DIDN'T NOTICE THE DRIVER.

NO.

DID BUDDY LOOK SCARED AS HE GOT IN THE CAR? LIKE HE DIDN'T WANT TO GO?

NO. HE WAS OPENING THE DOOR AND GETTING IN.

DID YOU RECOGNIZE THE CAR? HAVE YOU SEEN IT AROUND HERE BEFORE?

I...

I DON'T KNOW. IT WAS JUST A CAR.

ANY MORE QUESTIONS?

JUST A COUPLE.

JORDAN, I KNOW WE'VE ASKED YOU THIS BEFORE.

BUT ARE YOU **POSITIVE** YOU DIDN'T SEE THE DRIVER? NOT EVEN WHETHER IT WAS A MAN OR A WOMAN?

I WAS LOOKING AT **BUDDY,** NOT THE DRIVER.

ONE LAST THING.

ABOUT WHAT TIME DID YOU SEE BUDDY GET INTO THE CAR?

MOM, WHAT TIME DID MRS. KATZ PICK ME UP?

11:15, HONEY.

11:15, THEN. MY PIANO LESSON WAS AT 11:30.

scribble

AS FOR ME, THE POLICE MOSTLY HAD QUESTIONS ABOUT MR. BARRETT.

THEY SEEMED DISAPPOINTED WHEN I SAID I DIDN'T KNOW MUCH ABOUT HIM, OR HIS DIVORCE WITH MRS. BARRETT...

BUT THEY WERE **VERY** INTERESTED WHEN THEY FOUND OUT THAT MRS. BARRETT DIDN'T WANT MR. BARRETT CALLING THE KIDS.

DAWN?

MARNIE WILL BE AWAKE SOON.

I SHOULD GET BACK TO WORK.

YOU'RE A BRAVE GIRL. I'M VERY PROUD OF YOU.

SHOULD'VE SEEN ME BEFORE YOU GOT HERE.

WELL, JEFF AND I WILL BE HELPING WITH THE NEIGHBORHOOD SEARCH, SO...

JUST YELL IF YOU NEED ANYTHING.

THANKS, MOM.

FOR THE NEXT HOUR, THE POLICE CAME AND WENT.

THEY SEARCHED THE HOUSE FOR AN ADDRESS BOOK OR ANY CLUE AS TO WHERE MR. BARRETT MIGHT BE, BUT DIDN'T FIND MUCH.

MALLORY VOLUNTEERED TO LOOK AFTER SUZI AT THE PIKES' HOUSE, AND I CALLED TO SEE IF SUZI REMEMBERED WHERE HER DAD LIVED.

UM...IN HIS 'PARTMENT?

WHILE ALL OF THIS WAS GOING ON, I STILL HAD MARNIE TO LOOK AFTER.

ring ring rin

SO YOU'RE TELLING ME THAT MY EX-HUSBAND... **TOOK**...BUDDY THIS MORNING.

AND YOU DIDN'T KNOW UNTIL **BUDDY** CALLED?

THAT'S CORRECT. I DON'T MEAN TO ALARM YOU...

BUT HAS YOUR DIVORCE BEEN A FRIENDLY ONE?

NO, IT HASN'T. WHY?

BECAUSE, WELL, A LOT OF MISSING KIDS ARE CHILDREN OF DIVORCE.

THEY'VE BEEN TAKEN BY PARENTS WHO WANT CUSTODY, BUT HAVEN'T BEEN GRANTED IT.

OH, **NO.** HAM AND I HAVE PROBLEMS, BUT HE'D NEVER **KIDNAP** THE KIDS. I MEAN, HE ALREADY GETS THEM TWICE A...

TWICE A...

SCOOT

OOPS.

slam
tptptp
thud

DAWN!

BUDDY!

I'M SORRY I MADE YOU WORRY.

I'M **STARVING.** DO WE HAVE COOKIES?

LET'S SEE WHAT WE CAN FIND.

WHILE BUDDY AND I WENT ON OUR LITTLE MISSION, THE POLICE GOT THE FULL STORY OUT OF MR. BARRETT.

MRS. BARRETT HAD BEEN MIXING UP THEIR SCHEDULE A LOT, AND WHEN HE REALIZED THAT SHE HAD CONFUSED THE DATES AGAIN TODAY, HE GOT MAD.

HE DECIDED TO TEACH HER A LESSON.

HIS PLAN WAS TO COME BY, TAKE THE KIDS, AND WAIT FOR MRS. BARRETT TO FIGURE OUT HER MISTAKE.

WHEN HE SAW BUDDY ALL BY HIMSELF, HE THOUGHT IT'D BE EASIEST TO JUST TAKE HIM.

HAM83

THEY WENT TO LUNCH AND A THEME PARK, BUT BUDDY DIDN'T SEEM HAPPY.

WHEN MR. BARRETT ASKED WHAT WAS WRONG, BUDDY SAID HE WAS WORRIED ABOUT **ME**, BECAUSE I DIDN'T KNOW WHERE HE WAS.

THAT WAS WHEN MR. BARRETT REALIZED THAT HIS EX-WIFE WASN'T EVEN HOME.

AND WHO KNEW WHAT A BABY-SITTER WOULD DO WHEN SHE FOUND OUT ONE OF HER CHARGES WAS MISSING?

THE POLICE GAVE MR. BARRETT A WARNING, BUT THAT WAS IT.

THEY DID STRONGLY SUGGEST, HOWEVER, THAT THE BARRETTS TALK TO THEIR LAWYERS ABOUT THEIR CUSTODY ARRANGEMENTS.

BUT THAT WASN'T QUITE THE END OF IT.

I HAD SOMETHING TO TELL MRS. BARRETT.

I WENT OVER THE NEXT MORNING.

MRS. BARRETT HAD SUGGESTED THAT MR. BARRETT TAKE THE KIDS FOR THE DAY, AND I'D NEVER HEARD THE HOUSE SO QUIET.

IT WAS WEIRD.

SO, DAWN, WHAT IS IT YOU WANTED TO TALK ABOUT?

WELL...

I REALLY LIKE BUDDY, MARNIE, AND SUZI, BUT...

I CAN'T BABY-SIT FOR THEM ANYMORE.

YOU **CAN'T?** IT'S NOT BECAUSE OF WHAT HAPPENED YESTERDAY, IS IT?

um...

WE'RE GOING TO STRAIGHTEN OUR PROBLEMS OUT, DAWN.

WE'RE GOING TO TALK TO OUR LAWYERS, AND MAYBE A COUNSELOR, TOO.

YOU WON'T HAVE ANY MORE ISSUES WITH MY EX-HUSBAND.

THAT'S NOT REALLY...

THE PROBLEM IS, UH...

I'VE HAD A LOT OF TROUBLE BECAUSE OF...

BECAUSE OF MISTAKES YOU'VE MADE.

I CAN'T BE A GOOD BABY-SITTER UNLESS THE PARENTS GIVE ME A LITTLE HELP.

I NEED TO KNOW THE IMPORTANT THINGS, LIKE ALLERGIES, AND WHERE YOU ARE WHILE I'M IN CHARGE. I NEED PHONE NUMBERS, AND ORGANIZATION.

I CAN'T DO ALL THE HOUSEWORK. AND YESTERDAY WAS VERY SCARY.

BUT MOST OF ALL...

BUDDY AND SUZI ARE STARTING TO DEPEND ON ME A LOT.

BUDDY COMES TO ME WITH SCHOOL PROBLEMS.

SUZI CALLS ME ON THE PHONE.

I LOVE BUDDY AND SUZI. AND MARNIE, TOO. BUT...

YOU'RE THEIR MOTHER... NOT ME.

SO I'LL BE SITTING FOR THEM THREE MORE TIMES.

I THINK IT WAS VERY BRAVE OF YOU TO HAVE THE TALK IN THE FIRST PLACE.

YEAH. YOU CAME TO A REASONABLE COMPROMISE.

HOW ARE THE KIDS DOING NOW, ANYWAY? SINCE THE INCIDENT?

THEY'RE GOOD, I THINK. MARNIE'S TOO LITTLE TO REMEMBER...

MALLORY TOOK GREAT CARE OF SUZI WHILE THINGS WERE GOING DOWN...

AND BUDDY'S OKAY.

HE'S CONFUSED, BUT HIS PARENTS EXPLAINED THAT THEY HAVE SOME PROBLEMS THEY'RE WORKING ON.

THE IDEA OF PARENTS KIDNAPPING THEIR OWN CHILDREN IS SCARY.

YEAH.

MY DECISION...

IS TO RAISE OUR CLUB DUES.

WHAT?

THE ONLY SOLUTION I CAN THINK OF IS TO PAY SOMEONE TO DRIVE ME TO AND FROM CLUB MEETINGS. NOT A CAB DRIVER, BUT SOMEONE WHO'D LIKE TO EARN A LITTLE EXTRA MONEY.

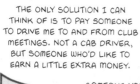

SOMEONE YOUNG WHO'S JUST LEARNED TO DRIVE --

CHARLIE!

CHARLIE WILL BE ABLE TO DRIVE THEN, WON'T HE?

KRISTY, THAT'S A GREAT IDEA!

AND I BET HE'LL BE **DYING** FOR EXCUSES TO USE THE CAR.

BUT...DO YOU MIND PAYING FOR IT OUT OF OUR DUES?

I KNOW IT'S KIND OF --

KRISTY, YOU'RE THE **PRESIDENT.**

IT'S THE PERFECT SOLUTION.

NO KRISTY...

NO CLUB.

ANN M. MARTIN'S The Baby-sitters Club is one of the most popular series in the history of publishing – with more than 176 million books in print worldwide – and inspired a generation of young readers. Her novels include *Belle Teal, A Corner of the Universe* (a Newbery Honor book), *Here Today, A Dog's Life,* and *On Christmas Eve,* as well as the much-loved collaborations, *P.S. Longer Letter Later* and *Snail Mail No More,* with Paula Danziger, and *The Doll People* and *The Meanest Doll in the World,* written with Laura Godwin and illustrated by Brain Selznick. She lives in upstate New York.

GALE GALLIGAN is a graduate of NYU and the Savannah College of Art and Design. Her comics nave appeared in a number of anthologies, and she worked as a production assistant of *Drama* by Raina Telgemeier. Gale lives in Pleasantville, New York. Visit her online at www.galesaur.com.

DON'T MISS THE OTHER
BABY-SITTERS CLUB GRAPHIC NOVELS!

A GRAPHIC NOVEL FROM THE BESTSELLING AUTHOR OF *SMILE*
RAINA TELGEMEIER
THE BABY-SITTERS CLUB

KRISTY'S GREAT IDEA
BASED ON THE NOVEL BY
ANN M. MARTIN

A GRAPHIC NOVEL FROM THE BESTSELLING AUTHOR OF *SMILE*
RAINA TELGEMEIER
THE BABY-SITTERS CLUB

THE TRUTH ABOUT STACEY
BASED ON THE NOVEL BY
ANN M. MARTIN

A GRAPHIC NOVEL FROM THE BESTSELLING AUTHOR OF *SMILE*
RAINA TELGEMEIER
THE BABY-SITTERS CLUB

MARY ANNE SAVES THE DAY
BASED ON THE NOVEL BY
ANN M. MARTIN

A GRAPHIC NOVEL FROM THE BESTSELLING AUTHOR OF *SMILE*
RAINA TELGEMEIER
THE BABY-SITTERS CLUB

CLAUDIA AND MEAN JANINE
BASED ON THE NOVEL BY
ANN M. MARTIN